Talking Trees

The Real Story

by

Michelle Hinkson Gaskin

DORRANCE
PUBLISHING CO
EST. 1920
PITTSBURGH, PENNSYLVANIA 15238

Dorrance Publishing Co
585 Alpha Drive
Suite 103
Pittsburgh, PA 15238
Visit our website at *www.dorrancebookstore.com*

ISBN: 978-1-6376-4409-6
eISBN: 978-1-6376-4440-9

Talking Trees

The Real Story

Who's the father?

I need a pedicure but Covid.

Prospecting

Take smaller bites

Are you looking at me?

Social distancing

This centipede is climbing up the wrong tree.

How rude!

Of course he's your kid.

In an octopus' garden in the shade

Bear with me

Alien vs. Predator?

I spotted … two giraffes

Unsupervised kitchen

Hole in 1

Hold on, don't look down...

Sssssssss

It's hard work getting to the top.

Lean back ... lean back

Tell me, does this look stupid?

I've fallen and I can't get up!

Not above climbing your back on the way to the top

A "rear" view

Whooooooo is it?

26

Finally ... no humans

You're all trunk, no elephant.

Alright, I'm leafing!

Who's green with envy?

Reaching ... almost got it

Make a wish